Adventure Story Bible
Book 19

The Early Years of Jesus

Written by Anne de Graaf

Illustrated by José Pérez Montero

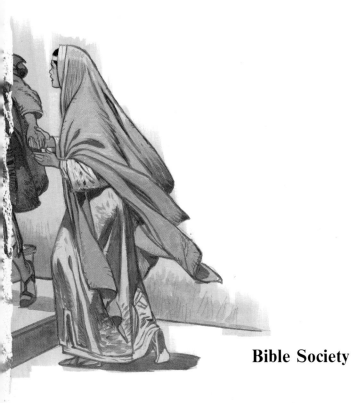

Bible Society

The Early Years of Jesus

Contents — Isaiah 11—12; Luke 1—5; Matthew 1—4.14;
Psalm 139; Mark 1.6; John 1—2

Introduction to the New Testament

In the Old Testament God taught his people the difference between right and wrong. He gave them laws to help them know the right way to live. He sent them leaders to show them the right way. When they went wrong he eventually brought them back, even though it was often a painful process.

But there was one problem: nobody is perfect. God knew this. So everyone would keep going wrong, and needing to be brought back. The people needed something completely new. A new picture of what it meant to live God's way. A new power to live like that. A new way to listen to God and to know that he would forgive them if they did go wrong.

That was why Jesus, who we call God's Son, came into the world and into the story. Jesus showed people what God was like. He was perfect. He healed sick people and did other miraculous things. He helped people learn about God. Finally he showed how much it costs for God to forgive us, by dying so that we could always be forgiven. Then he came alive to show that life with God never ends.

The New Testament tells us all this story, and also how Jesus' closest friends used the new power he brought to tell everyone the good news of forgiveness and new life. So the Christian Church spread and spread, as it still does today, all round the world.

Introduction to the Gospels

In the Bible there are four separate books about Jesus — what he did and said, and how he died and rose again to life. They are all called "Gospels", which means "good news", and each one is named after one of Jesus' followers.

Matthew's book tells us about what Jesus taught, particularly to the Jewish people he lived with. *Mark's* book shows us Jesus in action, all the places he visited and the things he did. *Luke* was a doctor, and so his book describes how Jesus cared for the sick and lonely. *John's* book explains more about the things Jesus taught, and about the amazing, powerful person Jesus was.

THE PROMISED KING

Waiting for the Messiah

Isaiah 11.1–12.6; Luke 1.1–4

The Jews knew that one day God would send a Messiah to save them. "Messiah" is a Hebrew word which means "The Anointed One," or someone who has the power of God with him. The Messiah would bring God close to his people. Jesus came to be the Messiah and Saviour for everyone.

A Jewish prophet called Isaiah had spoken about the coming of a Messiah. His words are written in the Old Testament, and the Jews knew them well. They said that the coming Messiah would belong to the family of David — a great king of Israel who lived hundreds of years before the time of Jesus. The Messiah would be wise and understanding, and would know good from evil. He would look after the poor and bring peace.

When Jesus came he was just as Isaiah had described the Messiah. Luke's book about Jesus reminds everyone that Isaiah had said this, so that people can understand who Jesus is.

God promises a baby

Luke 1.5-25

When Jesus was born, Israel was part of the Roman Empire. The Romans were a very powerful nation who ruled many of the countries around the Mediterranean Sea. Sometimes they allowed the people who lived in those countries to have their own kings.

While Herod was king in Israel, an old priest named Zechariah lived in Judaea, the southern part of the country. He and his wife Elizabeth were good people who tried hard to obey God's laws. They had wanted a baby for many years. But they grew older, and still no children came.

One day Zechariah was doing his work as a priest in the Temple in Jerusalem, taking his turn in the daily service. He was chosen to burn the incense, which made a pleasant smell that helped the Jews to worship God. While he was in the Temple, and crowds of people were praying outside, an angel appeared before him. Zechariah was afraid. He didn't know what to do because he had never seen an angel before!

"Don't be frightened, Zechariah," the angel said. "God has heard your prayers and knows how badly you want a child. Elizabeth will have a baby son and you will give him the name John. This baby will be special because he will help bring many people back to God. He will be filled with the Holy Spirit, and God will use him in a very important way. He will speak God's own words as he helps the people get ready for the Lord."

Zechariah was amazed at what he heard. It seemed too good to be true. He just could not believe that his wife, who was so old, would be able to have a child. So he asked the angel, "How will I know that this is true? We are both so old."

The angel said, "I am Gabriel, who stands in the presence of God. Because

you do not believe me, you will not be able to speak until the baby is born."

When Zechariah went outside he could not talk. He jumped up and down and waved his hands, trying to tell the people what had happened to him. When they realized that he could not speak, they knew he had seen a vision.

Zechariah went home to Elizabeth. Soon afterwards, just as Gabriel had said, Elizabeth became pregnant. She would have a baby after all! Elizabeth and Zechariah were so happy.

An angel visits a young woman

Luke 1.26–38

When Elizabeth was six months pregnant, God sent the angel Gabriel, the same angel who had appeared to Zechariah, to a young woman called Mary. Like Zechariah, Mary had not seen an angel before, and she wondered what was happening. "Peace be with you!" said Gabriel. "The Lord is with you, and has been good to you!"

Mary was scared. Why was the angel saying this to her? What could he possibly mean?

"Do not be afraid, Mary," said Gabriel. "You have been chosen by God to be the mother of his Son, and you will call him Jesus. He will be great, and God will be with him."

Mary was probably about fifteen years old. It was not unusual then for girls to be engaged at that age, and Mary was going to marry a man called Joseph. She heard the angel's words and thought to herself, "Any girl who is going to have a baby and is not married will be in trouble." She knew Joseph might not want to marry her if she was going to have a baby.

But instead of arguing with the angel or doubting what he said, Mary said, "Yes, I am here to do what God wants." She knew God loved her and would take care of her.

God would cause his own Son to grow inside Mary, and be born, just like any other baby.

A journey over the hills

Luke 1.39–56

Soon afterwards Mary left her home in Nazareth, in Galilee, and travelled south to Judaea to visit her old friend and relative, Elizabeth. As she crossed the hills and watched the sun go down in a rainbow of colours, she wondered why God had chosen her to be the mother of his child. He was so great he made the sun set every night, then rise in the morning. And she was just an ordinary girl.

Mary did not really understand it all. But she was excited. She had chosen to obey God, and even though she might not know how everything would work out, Mary did know God was in control. And that was what mattered.

When Mary arrived at the home of Elizabeth and Zechariah, she called out, "Hello, Elizabeth!"

At the sound of Mary's voice, Elizabeth's baby moved inside her. Elizabeth said, "Mary, you are blessed by God, you are the mother of my Lord! I know this because when you called out, my own baby jumped for joy inside me. You are very special indeed, because God's Son lives in you."

Knowing that Elizabeth shared her wonderful secret made Mary feel so happy, she wanted to sing. "My heart is so happy, because God is so great. He makes mighty rulers fall. He saves the poor and humble. He has remembered his people and the promise he made to them so long ago. He will help Israel again!" Elizabeth looked at Mary and smiled while she sang.

Mary stayed with Elizabeth for three months, until Elizabeth's baby was almost due to be born. During that time they talked about their babies and looked forward to the days when they could hold their children in their arms and love them.

"My son is called John!"

Luke 1.57–79

In all this time, Zechariah had not been able to talk because he had not believed the angel Gabriel. He was very happy that his wife was pregnant, and he looked forward to the baby being born so that he could talk again.

The day finally came for Elizabeth to have her baby. It was a little boy with sparkling dark eyes. All the neighbours and family were so happy for Elizabeth and Zechariah, they laughed and sang with them.

When the boy was eight days old, it was time to give him a name. In those days most people named a son after his father, but before the friends and family could do this, Elizabeth said, "No, his name is John."

"What's this?" they murmured. "There is no one in the family with that name. Why would she want to call the baby John?" To make sure, they asked Zechariah what he thought.

Because he could not talk, he wrote down on a piece of stone, "His name is John." They were all astonished.

What was even more astonishing was that the minute Zechariah finished writing, he opened his mouth and could talk again! The first thing he said was how great God was. He thanked God for his son, who would grow into a prophet for God, preparing the way for the Lord, the one who would come and save God's people.

But the people who heard him were afraid. "What is this child going to be?" they asked. They could see that God was watching over the baby boy.

"How shall I tell Joseph?"

Matthew 1.18–19

When Mary returned to Nazareth after visiting
Elizabeth, she knew she would have to tell
Joseph that she was expecting a baby. She
prayed that God would prepare him for the
news. Mary loved Joseph and did not want
him to be upset.

When Joseph came to see her Mary prayed,
"Lord, please help him to understand."

"Joseph, something has happened which is
hard to believe, but it's true," Mary said. "You
know how our fathers and their fathers have
been waiting for so many years, hoping the
promised Messiah would come to save Israel?
He was to be born in your family, descended
from King David."

Joseph nodded. He wondered why Mary
looked so serious, and why she was telling
him all this.

"Well," Mary continued, "God has blessed
me very much. I don't really know why, but
he has chosen me to be the mother of the
Messiah, his Son. The baby inside me is
already three months old." Mary held her
breath, hoping that Joseph would understand.

"Oh, Mary..." Joseph turned away from her.

"I love her so much," he thought. "But I cannot marry her now she is expecting a baby which isn't mine." Her story sounded too amazing to be true.

He looked back at her again. Mary's eyes shone with confidence, yet he could not believe such a strange story. Joseph walked away from her, trying to think how he could call off the wedding without hurting Mary too much. All the hopes and dreams he had built up around their life together began to fade.

Joseph's dream

Matthew 1.20-24; Psalm 139.1-18

One night soon afterwards, an angel of the Lord appeared to Joseph in a dream. "Son of David, do not be afraid to make Mary your wife. She speaks the truth. The baby she carries is a gift from God himself. He will save his people from their sins. You are to call him Jesus."

When Joseph woke up, he chose to believe the message.

He went to Mary and told her that he would still like to marry her. Mary was overjoyed, and thanked God. A short time later, Joseph and Mary were married.

They spent the next few months waiting together for the birth of Jesus. They often thought about the baby that God had given them.

A Psalm of David, written long ago, says that the Lord knows us inside out. God understands even those things we puzzle over. When a baby grows inside his or her mother, God knows and loves that baby from the beginning. King David said there was no place far enough away or dark enough where we could hide from God's love.

There in the village of Nazareth, God was making his Son grow inside Mary. Soon Jesus the Saviour would be born.

11

GOD KEEPS HIS PROMISE

Jesus is born

Matthew 1.25; Luke 2.1–7

It was very early in the morning. The sun had not yet risen. Joseph leaned over Mary and shook her softly. "It will soon be time to go, Mary. Wake up."

Joseph had waited until the last possible moment. The donkey had all they needed packed on to it. They had a long journey ahead of them and needed an early start.

Mary opened her eyes. "Yes, I'm coming," she said. She got ready, then went out to Joseph who helped her on to the donkey, in between the bundles he had packed.

Joseph and Mary were going to Bethlehem in Judaea. The Roman Emperor Augustus had told everyone to go back to the town where their family came from, so his soldiers could count the number of people in the tribes of Israel. Joseph's family came from Bethlehem, so that is where he had to go, together with Mary.

"I wish we didn't have to go today," Joseph said, "when the baby is so near to being born."

Mary nodded. She was finding it difficult to get comfortable on the donkey, because the baby had made her so large now. "This will be a long day," she thought to herself.

The hours passed. When the sun rose, it became hot. Mary wanted to go to sleep, but she was afraid she would fall off if she did!

She walked for a little while, but soon became so tired that Joseph put her back on the donkey.

Finally they arrived in Bethlehem. The streets were crowded. There seemed to be children running everywhere, and so much noise! Suddenly, Mary felt a tightening in her stomach. She knew what it meant.

"Joseph, the baby. I think the baby is coming soon!"

Joseph looked at her. "We have to get you somewhere quiet, out of all these crowds," he said, looking around.

The couple went from one inn to another, asking if they had a spare room, but everywhere was full up.

At one point, Joseph grew desperate. "Look," he cried. "My wife is close to having her baby!" The man he spoke to looked at Mary.

He could see that the baby was going to be born soon.

"Yes," he said. "You need to find somewhere quickly. My inn is full, but as you need somewhere so urgently, you could use my stable. You will at least be out of the crowds. I doubt if you'll find anywhere else soon enough.

Joseph shouted his thanks over his shoulder as he ran to take Mary to the stable.

Once Mary was safely there, Joseph relaxed. He felt sorry that his wife would have her baby in a stable where animals lived, but they didn't have much choice.

It was a long night. While the baby was being born, Joseph helped Mary in every way he could. Finally, Joseph held the tiny baby boy in his arms. He gave the little one to Mary. She looked up at Joseph with tears of joy in her eyes and said, "This is Jesus."

The shepherds

Luke 2.8-20

While Mary and Joseph took care of Jesus that night, a strange thing happened in the nearby hills. A group of shepherds who were taking care of their flocks of sheep during the night, saw an angel. They were very frightened. They had never seen an angel before, and the night became bright with the angel's presence.

The angel said, "Do not be afraid. I have got great news for you! A Saviour has been born tonight in Bethlehem. You will know it is true when you see a baby in a manger."

Then suddenly, there were angels all around the shepherds. The angels sang, "Glory to God in the highest, and peace on earth to all who please him."

When the angels left them the shepherds looked at each other in amazement. "Was it just a dream?" they asked. But they knew it was real. They thanked God for letting them see and hear such special things. "Let's go to Bethlehem and see if we can find the baby who is to be our Saviour," they said. So they hurried into the town. Soon they found Mary and Joseph, and the baby was lying in a manger just as the angel had said! They told Mary and Joseph about the angel's message, then they knelt and worshipped Jesus as Saviour and Lord. Mary and Joseph watched them. Mary thought hard about what had happened, and what had been said. She knew she would never forget that night.

An old man's wish comes true

Luke 2.21-38

When Jesus was eight days old, his parents took him to the Temple so that he could be named and blessed. It was part of the Jewish Law that parents should do this. This was one of the rules that God had given to Moses, long ago. Parents should say thank you to God for their children.

When they had finished thanking God, they turned around and saw a very old man watching them. He was staring at the baby, who Mary held in her arms. Mary smiled at him and the old man came closer.

He reached out a hand to touch Jesus' head. Then he took the baby from Mary, and held him. "I thank you, Lord," he said. "Now I have seen the light which will show the whole world the way to God."

Joseph and Mary were amazed at what they heard the old man Simeon say. Simeon told them how God had promised him that he would not die until he had seen the Messiah. The Spirit of God had told Simeon the Saviour would be at the Temple that day.

"This is the Saviour," he said. "Because of Jesus many people will change their ways of thinking and turn to God. Others will hear his truth and turn away from God, showing what they are really like." Then he looked at Mary. "And as well as the joy that Jesus will bring you, you will have sorrow through what will happen to Jesus because of what he will say and do."

Then an old woman came towards them. Her name was Anna and she was blessed and used by God in a special way. She helped God's people by passing on his messages to them, pointing them back in God's direction. Anna's husband had died when they had been married for only seven years. Since then she had lived in the Temple, serving God and praying to him.

Anna looked down at the little baby lying in Simeon's arms and said, "Thank you, God. This is the one we have waited so long for. He will save Israel."

Mary turned to Joseph. So many things had happened since they had gone to Bethlehem, and it was hard to take in what everyone had been saying about Jesus. Joseph put his arm round Mary and, taking Jesus, they left the Temple.

The star that led to Jesus

Matthew 2.1-10

While all this was happening some wise men were on a journey, looking for Jesus. They came from far-away lands in the east. They studied stars and had seen a bright star in the night skies. Because of this the men believed something great had happened. So they travelled a long distance and eventually arrived in Jerusalem. When they got there they asked, "Does anyone know where we can find the baby who will be king of the Jews? We saw his star in the east and have come to worship him."

King Herod heard about their search and was very upset to think that a baby had been born who was to be a king. But he knew nothing about Jesus' birth, so he called in the religious leaders. "Where is the Messiah, the king of the Jews, supposed to be born?" he asked.

"In Bethlehem," they answered. They knew the answer because that was what the prophets had said many years earlier. When Herod heard this he called the wise men to a secret meeting. "When did the star appear?" he asked them. When he found out all he wanted to know, he sent them to go and look for the new king in Bethlehem. "Go and honour him," Herod said. "And when you have found him, come and tell me, so that I can do the same."

The wise men went on to Bethlehem. On the way they saw the same star that they had seen in the east. This made them very excited. "We're on the right path to the king," they said. They followed the star until it stopped over the place where Jesus had been born. When they went inside and saw Jesus in Mary's arms, they were very happy. Their long journey had been worthwhile. They had found the king!

Gifts for a king

Matthew 2.11–12

The visitors unloaded their camels and brought rare and beautiful gifts to Jesus. Mary and Joseph were amazed. "These are gifts fit for a king," Mary whispered to Joseph.

One of the visitors bowed before Jesus. "We have travelled a long way, knowing a king of the Jews was soon to be born. We saw his star in the east, and it has led us to you. Here is gold for a great king." He put the gold beside Jesus.

The second visitor knelt before Jesus. "It is not usual for such a large star suddenly to appear. This baby will be the greatest of all men." He laid a jar of myrrh in front of Jesus. Myrrh is a very valuable perfume which could be used as a medicine, and was also used by Jews in preparing bodies to be buried.

The third visitor came and knelt before Jesus. "This is incense for burning. It will make the air sweet. Incense pleases God."

They all thanked God for bringing Jesus into the world. Mary and Joseph thanked the men for their presents, and they looked at Jesus, wondering what plans God had for him.

The travellers stayed with Mary and Joseph and told them about the lands they came from. The night before they were due to go back home, the visitors had a dream in which God warned them not to go back and see King Herod. So they went home, taking a different route from the one by which they had come.

Escape to Egypt

Matthew 2.13–18

After the visitors left Mary and Joseph, the family rested. Jesus slept, fed, and grew.

One night, Joseph had a dream. An angel of the Lord came to him and said, "Wake up. Take the child and his mother and run away to Egypt. Stay there until I tell you to leave. King Herod is going to look for the child. He wants to kill him."

Joseph woke up with a start. In the past days he had seen how God's hand was on all that was happening. Everything from finding a place for Mary to have the baby to the visit by the wise men had seemed like one miracle after another.

Joseph woke Mary up and told her about the dream. They quickly packed up their few things and put them on the donkey. Joseph gently lifted the sleeping Jesus and put him into Mary's arms. He led the donkey out, and they disappeared into the dark night.

Meanwhile, King Herod had waited and waited for the wise men to return from their visit. When they did not arrive, he grew angry. He had wanted to trick them into telling him where the new king was, but they had tricked him instead.

"They were to tell me where this king of the Jews is. And now they are gone and I don't know!" he shouted at his servants.

Herod did not like the idea of another king. He wanted to be the only king.

"Whoever this king of the Jews is, I will kill him! I may not know where he is, but I know he is still just a baby!"

Herod ordered a terrible thing. He told his soldiers to go out into Bethlehem, and kill every baby boy they could find who was two years old and younger. No matter how much

the mothers and fathers cried and begged, the soldiers would not let the children live. They tramped in and out of homes, looking for baby boys. But they did not find Jesus. Jesus was safe with Joseph and Mary, on the way to Egypt.

JESUS GROWS UP
Back home to Nazareth

Matthew 2.19–23; Luke 2.39

Several years passed, and the wicked King Herod finally died. Joseph had led Mary and Jesus safely to Egypt, and there they lived, waiting for a word from God to tell them that they could return to Israel.

One night, an angel of the Lord again appeared to Joseph in a dream. "Wake up and take the child and his mother back to Israel because those who wanted to kill him are dead," the angel said.

The next morning Joseph told Mary the good news. They were soon on their way back home. But when they arrived in the part of Israel called Judaea they heard that Herod's son, Herod Archelaus, was in power. Everyone said he was just as bad and cruel as his father had been. So Joseph moved his little family north to Galilee.

They went back to their old village, Nazareth. There, in the spring–time, the flowers cover the hills with colour.

In Nazareth Joseph had a carpenter's shop. People came to him with their broken chairs and tables. Joseph sawed and hammered all day, carving wood into furniture. As Jesus grew up, he often came in the shop to watch Joseph. When Joseph asked him to help, Jesus would hand Joseph the tools he needed.

In the evenings Joseph and Mary taught Jesus the Jewish history, and about loving God. But all along, Joseph and Mary had the feeling that their little boy already knew a great deal about God. They noticed when Jesus was still quite young that he was very wise. The family enjoyed being together, and learned from each other.

Joseph and Mary lose Jesus

Luke 2.41–52

When Jesus was twelve, he was old enough to take part in Jewish religious life. So Mary and Joseph took him to Jerusalem for the Passover festival. The city was full of people. Tens of thousands crowded the streets. Donkeys and camels seemed to be everywhere.

On the last day of the festival Mary and Joseph left to go home. They both thought Jesus was in another part of the group from Galilee, among their relatives and friends who were going back to Nazareth.

After a whole day of travelling, they asked the other children from the group, "Have you seen Jesus?" The children shook their heads.

Mary and Joseph looked at each other, and they began to be frightened. Jesus was still back in Jerusalem! How would they ever find him? They left the group and hurried back to the city. There they looked everywhere for him. He was not in the market, where so many people called out in loud voices. Mary and Joseph saw many children, but Jesus was not among them.

For three days they searched high and low. They asked everyone they saw, "Have you seen a boy, about so high, and with dark hair?" But no one had.

Mary and Joseph felt desperate. They had lost their precious son. Finally, they went to the Temple where the Jewish people worshipped on the Sabbath and holy days.

When they entered, they saw another huge crowd of people. Joseph looked from one corner to the other until, finally, he spotted a little group of Jewish teachers sitting together and talking. There, in the middle of the group, sat Jesus. He was talking, too, and those who listened looked very interested in what he was saying.

Mary and Joseph pushed their way through the crush of people. When they reached him, Mary said, "My son, why didn't you try to find us? We have looked everywhere for you and have been very worried."

Jesus said, "Why didn't you know where to look? Didn't you know that I had to be in my Father's house?"

Mary and Joseph didn't understand that Jesus meant that since he was God's Son, the Temple was his Father's house. As they left the Temple with Jesus, they heard many people say, "How is it that such a young boy could have talked about the things he did with such understanding? He is more than clever, he is blessed with wisdom."

Jesus returned with his parents to Nazareth. He was a good boy and did what his parents told him. His parents loved him a great deal, and other people liked him, too. The older Jesus became, the more he understood about the ways of people and God. Mary watched him grow and was amazed all the time at how God's blessing was on him.

GETTING READY FOR THE KING

"Get ready!"

Matthew 3.1–12; Mark 1.1–8; Luke 3.1–18

While Jesus was growing up in Nazareth, his cousin John had been growing up in Judaea, with his parents Elizabeth and Zechariah.

Mary had never forgotten her visit to Elizabeth when Elizabeth was pregnant with John and Mary was pregnant with Jesus. John had jumped in Elizabeth's womb when Mary had arrived, and John and Jesus had a very special friendship. They were both close to God through his Holy Spirit.

When John grew to be a man he went off by himself into the desert. He prayed there, growing closer to God. God gave John a special message and told him to tell the people what he said.

When John came to Judaea he was dressed like the old prophet Elijah, in a camel-hair cloak and leather belt. John was used to eating insects and wild honey. He was very different from other people.

At first, crowds gathered to stare at the strange man, but then they came to hear him preach. John had a message from God, and when he spoke it sounded as though God himself was speaking through him. People listened to John and believed what he was saying.

"Get ready!" he called out to the people. "Get ready for the one who is coming! He will choose between those who live good lives and those who live bad lives!"

"What should we do to get ready?" the people asked.

"Think about what you are like and what you do, and say you're sorry for all the wrong things you have ever done! Turn back to God and change your lives!"

The people did as John said, because they believed what he was saying. Once they had said they were sorry, John asked them to come down to the river to be baptized. As they came out of the water, it was an outward sign of how God's forgiveness washes people clean from their sins, the bad things they have done. These people were starting their lives again. Being baptized showed that they were following God.

John explained how it was not just the water which wiped away their sins. "Someday there will be one who comes here and makes you clean on the inside. I baptize with water, but he will baptize with the Holy Spirit," John said.

The Holy Spirit helps people live as God wants them to. John meant that when Jesus baptized with God's Spirit, God's forgiveness and holiness would cover them, just as the water had.

The people wondered who John could be talking about. Would it be another great prophet, or could it be the Messiah?

Jesus is baptized

Matthew 3.13–17; Mark 1.9–11; Luke 3.21–22

Many people lined up to be baptized by John in the river. The crowds sat on the bank of the river, listening to him. Over and over again he told the people coming to him, "Say you're sorry. The time is coming soon when people will see that God is king, and how he wants you to live. Live a new life, don't do wrong things or hurt people any more."

John turned to the next person who wanted to be baptized. His eyes met Jesus' eyes and the cousins looked at each other.

Jesus said, "Baptize me, John."

"I should be the one baptized by you," John said. "Why do you come to me?"

"It is important that you baptize me," Jesus said. Jesus did not need to be forgiven for doing bad things. He was baptized because that was what God wanted. He was teaching by example what it meant to love and follow God.

So John did what Jesus asked. The crowd watched as Jesus went into the water. When he came out, he was praying. Suddenly, it seemed as though heaven had opened! God's Holy Spirit came down on Jesus, like a dove.

Then a voice came from heaven, "You are my Son. I love you, and you please me." The crowd did not fully understand what was happening, but in this way Jesus and the crowd knew that God was with him, and that he had the Holy Spirit in him.

John and Jesus looked long and hard at each other. They knew the meaning of the dove and God's message. They were like brothers, and loved each other very much. Both men knew there would be hard times ahead, but they loved God and that was what mattered.

Jesus and John

John 1.19–34

Once, when John the Baptist was preaching on the east side of the River Jordan, there was a group of religious leaders standing nearby who wanted to know whether John was really a prophet sent from God. The Jewish authorities in Jerusalem had sent them to find out. "Who is this strange man preaching by the river?" they asked each other.

Many people had come to hear John preach. The religious leaders, who were called priests and Levites, asked John, "Who are you?"

John said, "I am not the Messiah." John knew that Jesus was the Messiah, or Christ.

"Are you Elijah then, or the Prophet?"

"No," he answered.

They said, "Well who are you, then?"

John answered by quoting the prophet Isaiah, "I have come to tell people that the Lord is coming, and to help people be ready to listen to him and to follow him."

"But why are you baptizing, then, if you are not the Christ or the Prophet?" they said.

"I baptize in water," John said, but there is someone in this crowd who will come after me, and I'm not even good enough to be his servant."

A few days later John saw Jesus in the crowd again. He called out, "There is the Lamb of God who takes away the sin of the world! I've been using water to baptize you with, but there is someone here who will baptize you with God's Spirit! He is the Son of God, but you don't know him yet!"

When the priests and Levites heard John, they were confused and angry. They watched Jesus move through the crowd. "It is bad enough that John has so many people following him. But if this Jesus becomes even more popular than John, our problems are bigger than we think." They decided to keep an eye on them both.

Jesus is tempted

Matthew 4.1–12, 14.3–5; Mark 1.12–14, 6.17–20;
Luke 3.19–20, 4.1–13

After Jesus had been baptized in the river the
Holy Spirit led him into the desert. He was
full of the Holy Spirit. As Jesus came to earth
to show people the way back to God, the
devil wanted to stop what he was doing.

Jesus was the Son of God. He could have anything he wanted. The devil knew this. He wanted Jesus to choose to use his power in wrong ways. So the devil tempted Jesus.

Jesus was in the desert for forty days and nights. He had not eaten in all that time. This was Jesus' way of concentrating on God alone.

But the devil knew Jesus had gone without food, so he first tried to tempt Jesus with food. "If you are the Son of God, tell these stones to become bread."

The devil would have liked nothing better than for Jesus to say "Yes." But Jesus knew it was more important to do what God wanted. He also knew what God had said long ago to Moses. So Jesus answered by telling the devil what was already written in the Scriptures,

"People don't live just by having enough to eat. They also need to be near God and do what he says."

Then the devil led Jesus to Jerusalem and set him on the edge of the Temple roof. It was very high up. "Jump," the devil said. "If you are the Son of God, if God really loves you, he will send his angels to catch you."

"The Scriptures say, 'You should not test the Lord your God,'" Jesus said. "I'm not going to do what you want. I've come here to do what God wants!"

Lastly, the devil led Jesus to the top of a high place. He pointed to all the castles and far kingdoms of the world. "If you worship me," the devil said, "if you call me king, I will give all these to you."

Jesus told him that the Scriptures said that only God should be worshipped. He had come to earth to set up the Kingdom of God — a way of living which was as God wanted it to be — which lasts for ever. That was the only kingdom Jesus was interested in. "Go away," Jesus said to the devil. "I only serve the Lord God."

Then the devil left Jesus alone, and angels came to take care of him, because he was weak and hungry.

When Jesus left the desert he heard that John the Baptist had been put in prison by King Herod. John was being punished because he had told the king to stop living a bad life. John's followers told Jesus the news, and it made Jesus very sad.

JESUS BEGINS HIS WORK
The first followers of Jesus

John 1.35–50

Just before John the Baptist was taken prisoner he had told two of the men who had been learning from him to go and learn from Jesus. These two had heard Jesus speak and wanted to hear more. They found Jesus and started walking behind him until he turned and said, "What do you want?"

They asked if they could go to where he was staying that evening and listen to him teach. Jesus said, "Yes."

John's followers wanted to listen to Jesus because John had taught them to listen to the truth. John had said, "Someone greater than me is coming soon. Follow him."

They spent the rest of the day with Jesus, learning about God. One of the two who heard John speak and followed Jesus was Andrew. Andrew watched Jesus' face. His eyes were clear and he spoke gently, yet with great strength. "John says this is the Son of God," Andrew thought to himself. "If he is the one we have waited for all this time, then I must tell as many people as possible."

Andrew went to see his brother. "Simon!" he called. He ran up to his brother and grabbed him around the shoulders. "Simon, we've found the Messiah! Come on, Simon, and we'll take you to him."

Simon did not know what to think, but went to see Jesus. When Jesus saw Simon, he said, "You are Simon the son of John, but you will be called Cephas or Peter." The names Cephas and Peter both meant "Rock." This was the first time Jesus met Simon. Because of this meeting, Simon soon came to be called Simon Peter, or just Peter.

The next day Jesus decided to go into Galilee. While he was there he saw a man called Philip who came from the town where

Andrew and Peter lived. "Come with me," he said to him. So Philip went with Jesus.

After a while Philip then went to a friend called Nathanael and said, "We have found the person that Moses and the prophets spoke about. It is Jesus from Nazareth!"

Nathanael laughed at this. Nazareth was a small town, and he didn't think anyone important could come from there! "Come and see for yourself, then," Philip said. Nathanael went along with Philip, and when Jesus saw him he said, "I know you, Nathanael. You believe in God and try very hard to do what he wants." Nathanael was amazed and said, "How do you know me?" "I saw you sitting under the fig-tree, before Philip called you," Jesus said.

"Teacher," said Nathanael. "I believe that you are the Son of God, the king of Israel."

Jesus smiled at him. "Do you believe so easily? You will see greater things than these."

"Follow me!"

Matthew 4.18–22; Mark 1.16–20; Luke 5.1–11

After Andrew had brought Peter to meet Jesus, the two brothers returned home. They were fishermen and needed to take care of their boats and keep their nets mended in order to make a living. Peter could not get his meeting with Jesus out of his head.

"You really think he is the Messiah, don't you?" he asked his brother.

"I really do," Andrew answered.

"Who is Jesus, really?" Peter wondered. Then he looked up and to his surprise saw a huge crowd of people heading towards them.

"Here comes Jesus now!" Andrew shouted.

"Wait a minute!" Peter called to Andrew. "We have work to do. These nets must be washed."

But Jesus walked up to Peter and got into his boat, asking him to pull out a little way from the land. He sat down in the boat and began teaching the huge crowd which lined the shore.

"I won't get any work done today, that's for sure," Peter thought to himself.

When Jesus had finished speaking, he turned to Peter. "Go out into the deep water and let down your nets for a catch."

Peter said, "Teacher, we worked hard all night and caught nothing, but all right, I will do as you say."

When Peter dropped his net overboard and started to haul it in again he got the surprise of his life. It was full to bursting point! He called another boat to come and help him. By the time he and the other men had hauled all the fish on board, both boats were nearly sinking.

Peter was filled with amazement. He fell down at Jesus' feet and said, "You are the Lord! But you don't want to be with me. I'm not a good man at all, please just leave me alone!"

But Jesus said to him and Andrew, "Don't be afraid; from now on you will be catching men." Peter and Andrew looked at each other. They did not even need to argue about it. They put down their nets, pulled their boats up on the beach, left everything, and followed Jesus.

As they walked along the shore, the little group soon met Peter's partners, two brothers named James and John. Jesus went up to them. "Follow me," he said. So they left their father in the boat with the hired men, and went with Jesus.

These men became Jesus' closest friends. They followed him everywhere as he taught the people. They watched and learned from him. They were Jesus' helpers, his disciples.

"There's no more wine!"

John 2.1–13

A few days later, Jesus and his followers were invited to a wedding in Nathanael's home town of Cana. It was a big wedding and the party lasted several days. Jesus' mother Mary was there as well.

Mary knew her son was the Messiah. But the rest of the people did not know, and Jesus did not want them to know. Not yet. He wanted to teach them first about the ways they should be living and how God intended the people to follow the laws he gave to Moses long ago.

There were many people at the wedding. Food was heaped on the tables. There was meat and nuts, rice, cakes, and fruit.

All the guests drank a great deal of wine. Then, before the feast was over, the bridegroom noticed that there was no more wine. "Oh no," he thought to himself. "This is the worst thing that can happen!"

At Jewish weddings it was the bridegroom's job to make sure there was enough wine. If the wine ran out that meant the party might end early.

Mary saw the bridegroom's problem and went to Jesus. "They've run out of wine," she said.

Jesus said, "But why tell me? It's not yet time for me to show who I am."

But Mary called a servant, and told him to do what Jesus said. Jesus told the servant to fill six huge jars with water.

"Take out some water now and give it to the head waiter," he said, once the jars were full. The servant did this, and when the head waiter tasted the wine he went to the bridegroom.

"What have you done?" he asked him. "You have saved the best wine until last!" The bridegroom did not understand where this wine had come from, but Mary and the servants knew that Jesus had turned to the water into wine.

This was Jesus' first miracle. A miracle is something God makes happen, even though it may seem impossible. Jesus' miracles help people in need, and show that God loves them, and that Jesus has God's power in a very special way.

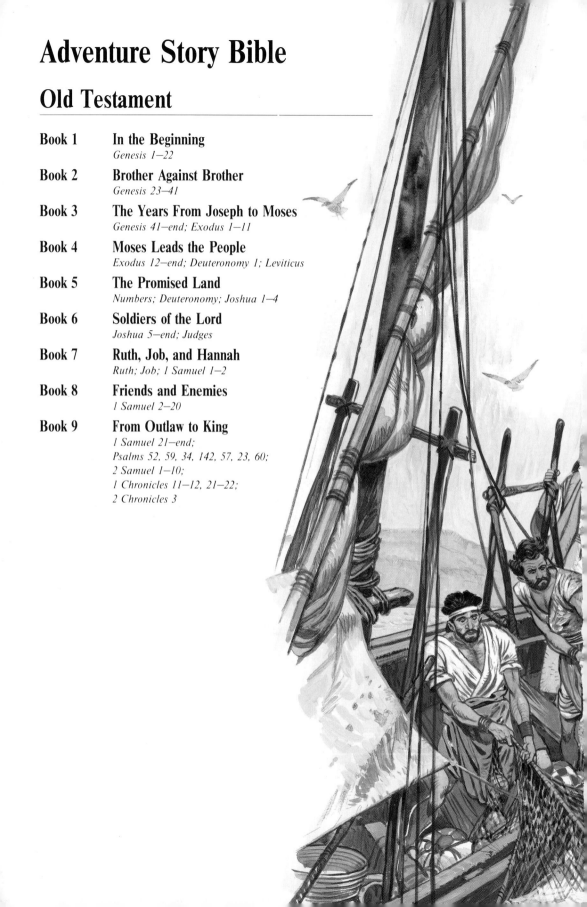

Adventure Story Bible

Old Testament

New Testament